I WAS BORN TO SUCKLE NIPPLES IN THE
MATERNITY WARDS OF NAPLES. I WAS BORN
TO DELIVER PIZZAS TO THE RED LIGHT DISTRICT
OF AMSTERDAM. I WAS BORN TO HURL HOT DOGS
IN THE GARAGE OF FARRAH FAWCETT'S MANSION.
I WAS BORN UNDER FLUORESCENT LIGHTING
TO A DOCTOR A LITTLE LOOSE WITH HIS SCALPEL.

I WAS BORN TO SWING LOUISVILLE SLUGGERS
AT PINATAS IN THE COURTYARDS OF MEXICO CITY.
I WAS BORN TO PLANT ROSES IN STEEL
& GIRDER CITIES SUFFERING FROM DRAUGHTS
& NATIONAL DEBT. I WAS BORN TO TWIRL
ABOUT THE STRATOSPHERE WITH SIGHTS
OF BRASIL IN MY STETHOSCOPE.

Ipanema, Rio de Janeiro

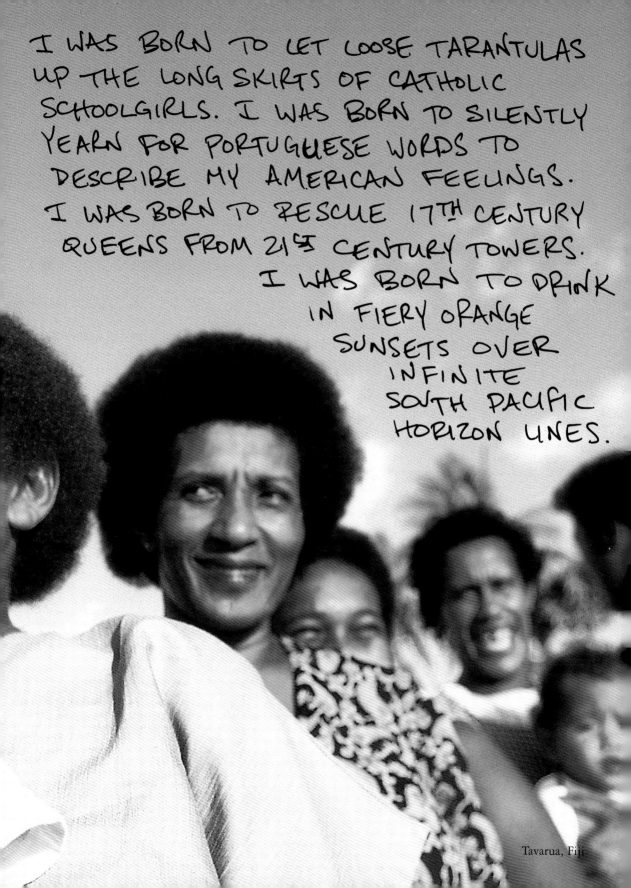

I WAS BORN TO LET LOOSE TARANTULAS UP THE LONG SKIRTS OF CATHOLIC SCHOOLGIRLS. I WAS BORN TO SILENTLY YEARN FOR PORTUGUESE WORDS TO DESCRIBE MY AMERICAN FEELINGS. I WAS BORN TO RESCUE 17TH CENTURY QUEENS FROM 21ST CENTURY TOWERS. I WAS BORN TO DRINK IN FIERY ORANGE SUNSETS OVER INFINITE SOUTH PACIFIC HORIZON LINES.

Tavarua, Fiji

I WAS BORN TO DANCE THE LAMBADA
THROUGH THE GATEWAYS OF ARMAGEDDON.
I WAS BORN FROM FERTILITY & THE PROMISE
OF A POST WWII AMERICAN DREAM.
I WAS BORN TO PEDDLE CIGARS IN THE
BACKSTREETS OF HAVANA. I WAS BORN
TO BLEED MONTBLANC INK & PERSPIRE
PABST BLUE RIBBON. I WAS BORN
TO WALK DOGS WHILE MICK JAGGER
SINGS ABOUT STRANGE STRAY CATS
I WAS BORN TO BE A HERO
FOR AN ETERNITY, A LIFE-
TIME, OR MAYBE JUST A DAY.

Occy's World Title, Rio

I WAS BORN TO DIE A GRANDIOSE DEATH POSSIBLY INVOLVING HEIGHTS, PROBABLY INVOLVING WATER, DEFINITELY INVOLVING ORGASM. I WAS BORN TO DRINK COFFEE COLORED FLESH + DREAM 3RD WORLD HALLUCINATIONS. I WAS BORN TO BE A BENEVOLENT, MOTORLESS EVEL KNIEVEL OF MY OWN DEVISING.

North Shore, Oahu

Millennium New Year, Paris

I WAS BORN TO ULTIMATELY FALL IN LINE WITH AGELESS WISDOM AND ALLOW THE WHOLE PROCESS TO REPEAT ITSELF.

WE APPROACH OUR MARTINIS
WITH SUCH HIGH EXPECTATIONS

JAMIE BRISICK

PRIMEIRO — ESPIRITO!
#1 - personalidade
#2 - cabeça
#3 - bunda e xoxota e
peitos
e
olhos
e
lábios
e
pernas
e
braços
e
ombros

GAROTA NATURAL

PRIMEIRO →

GISELLE BUNDCHEN

Pitangey

Um beijo e um abraço
MARY

#1
#3
#2

#4 →

1. Olha para os olhos
é lindo
2. Olha pelo peito lindo
3. Olha para

"um beijo
e um
Abraço
Killian'

BRASIL

BODY AND SOUL AT THE HEART OF RIO

"Selective breeding begins and ends with the ass. Forget about faces, forget about personalities, forget about what kind of family the person comes from. It's all much more primitive than this."

These were the words of Guga, my intensely Brasilian friend, as we strolled the sands of Ipanema Beach on a sunny afternoon just days before Carnaval. There were asses for miles, and they were as defined and pronounced as you could ever hope for good asses to be. They were asses that knew their place in life, asses of total certainty.

"Nowhere on the planet is the ass held in higher esteem than Brasil," he continued. "The tightness of the pants, the minimalism of the bathing suits...There's a well-known singer in Brasil, Carla Perez...her ass is so famous she's insured it for a million dollars!"

I took stock of the asses in our periphery, and wondered what a million dollar ass would look like.

"It makes great sense that they put the Ass on a pedestal here," I said to Guga. "I mean they're as poetic as they get right here on this beach. And they can bring on such a rainbow of emotions. For example," I said with a nod, "that one over there pulls out something very raw and cavemanish. I immediately imagine it in various bends and positions while that one over there," I pointed to another one, "I'm imaging what she looked like as a baby, what she'll look like when she's sixty, what her mother looks like, what our kids would look like. That one's more linked to the heart while the first one's more linked to the groin."

We walked in silence toward the nook of Aproador where runners, bikers and bladers would stop and catch their breaths before making their way back down the path. People work hard on their bodies in Rio. It's a city that places huge emphasis on the physical, and it made me wonder about the intentions of these sweating, panting people. Are their intentions to attempt to defy the aging process, to look good in the eyes of others? Or are they out here running, rollerblading, and bike riding 'cause it's fun and feels good? And does too much bodily consciousness hinder spiritual progress or does it make the vessel all the more prepared to ascend to thee?

The first time I really *felt* Rio was during a midday run on Barra Beach in the summer of '91. There were thousands of bronzed bodies sardine-canned from the street to the shoreline and I trotted my way through ankle-deep water, weaving in and out of bathers, surfers, soccer balls, *fresco bols*...I'd dart left to avoid a three-year old, right to make way for a wrinkled grandpa. There were dental-flossed, rock-hard *bundas* and Speedo'd, springy *futebol* legs; the entire spectrum of Rio life all speckled about the sand ('cause this is what *Cariocas* do on sunny summer days; they go to the beach). With a racing heartbeat and a stride that felt like Pele's, the balmy Atlantic crashing at my knees then receding back to its unknowable self, I felt for the first time *saudade*, a

Portuguese word meaning to miss, to long for. Now we've all missed our homes, or longed for a loved one, but *saudade*, to my interpretation, is more about missing out on a life never lived. Yes, I could move to Rio tomorrow and spend the rest of my days here, but this would not be the same as experiencing all rites of passage along the way—for example, learning to ride a bike on the swirling footpaths of Ipanema, or going to my first *futebol* game at Maracana with mom and dad, or giving up my virginity to the family's *mulatta* maid. I was not Brasilian and never would be. And for this I felt like I missed something.

Ten years later and I find myself thinking the exact same thing. Looking out over the stretch of Ipanema I saw nothing but animated beings talking, laughing and guzzling in the good life. There was a sexual vibrato in the air that was more energizing than fifty cups of coffee.

"Rio could be a great alternative to Viagra," Guga said in mockery of the American wonderdrug. "Just the very lifestyle here'll solve those same problems."

He had hit the nail on the head. This is the place to go if all seems a little lackluster, a little flaccid. And as the sun slipped behind that enormous, phallic rock to the south, and a rollerblader skated by, ass-shaking to the beat of her walkman, I concluded that the strange hunger I felt in my belly was not the need for a hamburger, but *saudade*, the desire to live a life in Rio from beginning to middle to end.

"A VIDA E COMO RAPADURA
E DOCE MAIS NAO E MOLE"
(LIFE IS LIKE A JAWBREAKER
IT'S SWEET BUT IT'S NOT EASY)

EU TENHO TESAO PARA CARNAVAL (I HAVE EXCITEMENT FOR CARNAVAL)

We're clowns, or at least all dressed up like clowns. This is the role we'll be playing for Mocidade Independente Samba School in Carnaval 2001. Here's how it works: The schools each have their theme/idea/allegory. They spend the entire year building floats and costumes and rehearsing songs and dances to support this. During the week of Carnaval, each school marches down the Sambodromo—a long strip of avenue lined with stadium-style bleachers filled with roughly 100,000 fans, freaks, celebrities, and judges who score each samba school based on their theme, floats, song, uniformity and overall style. To win is to be the toast of all of Brasil, so the amount of time, energy and emphasis put on Carnaval is massive. I came here planning to be a spectator. Somehow I got invited into the performance. Here's my account:

We take a bus from Ipanema to downtown Rio where it's a scattered mass of animation. The parks are filled with kids on swings, slides, jungle gyms; like nothing you'd ever see in rules and regulations-ridden USA. People bouncing about the streets— the costumed and well-to-dos mixed with the raggedy, barefooted *favela* (shantytown) folk. When we finally find *Mocidade* (all clad in the same clown costumes we are, like long lost family we never knew we had) they're all huddled under a gas station, a steady supply of beer flowing not from the pumps but from the make-shift mini-marts and mobile bartenders. The poor see Carnaval as prime time to earn a buck. You're constantly being hit up to buy a water or a beer. We fraternize with our fellow clowns and spend a long time lining up for last touches to our costumes. It's an elaborate process. *Fantasias* (the Portuguese word for costume) need much repair and added details like balloons and red ball noses.

My pal Morelo and I break from the bunch and go for a stroll. *Espirito* abounds. Pushing and shoving and *alegria*. Danger exists but somehow you don't feel it. The steady flow of *cerveja* definitely aids in these matters. On the one hand it makes you a sitting, very clumsy duck, on the other it loosens things up to match the whirlwind (approaching Carnaval stone cold sober is a bit like entering the freeway at 15 mph when your fellow drivers are all going 70). The biggest threat seems to be getting an eye poked out by the sharp edge of someone's four-foot in diameter costume. Or sitting in someone's piss.

The samba school directors are by far the most serious ones on the avenue. They police the parking lot that's been turned into a wardrobe department, making sure everyone's wearing their uniforms properly. A long line to get make-up done—only two women applying lipstick to literally hundreds (the same unsanitary stick, testament to the mind-over-matter mentality—germs? bacteria? *Carnaval'll kill 'em!*). It takes about two hours to get from costume/make-up to the holding bay of the Sambodromo. People trying to get around in their fantasias is like an episode of the Three Stooges. Headdresses tangle with one another, balloons pop, chunks of costume snap off through entranceways. Once in the holding bay the intensity of the directors becomes hyper-apparent.

They yell at us to get in formation—*rows of seven, even lines!* We wait around for over an hour; anxious, beer-drunk folk taking pisses the way horses do (no need to butt up in corners or shadows). We take a good look at the 30-foot high float we'll be marching behind. It's like an ornate, miniature city, like one of the rooms in Wonka's chocolate factory. All seems still and inanimate but upon closer inspection we notice little movements, little shuffles. At the center of the plumages are beautiful female faces twitching and trying to scratch itches. This is the backstage psyche-up before they go out and shake their wings for all the world to see. The entire year leads up to this—all the hard work that's gone into the floats, the costumes, the samba school theme song, the dances that go with the song, the entire idea that drives this particular school (in Mocidade's case: world peace)—and it's all reaching it's very apex at this very moment...

Things start to move. We begin to push forward, gaining momentum. As we enter the Sambodromo—our song in full swing, the volume turned way up—everyone turns electric and euphoric. All the preparation, all my thoughts that this is a lot of effort to go to for a fleeting hour-long march disappear as soon as we're illuminated by the lights of the Avenue. There are about a hundred thousand people on either side in the bleachers and *camarotes* (beer-sponsored perches) all swaying, most singing, and us—the 4,000 members of Mocidade—getting a small dose of what it's like to be The Rolling Stones or Michael Jackson or one of these big stadium bands. To the audience we must appear like one big technicolor herd but as far as I'm concerned I've got an intimate connection with every one of these spectators. We're samba-ing about at a crazed tempo; all of us squashing out our ulcers or whatever cancer cells might be brewing. There's a sense of revelation; the feeling that you can create the reality you choose. In other words, to some, Carnaval doesn't hold that much significance, but to the Brasilians, this is the be all and end all, and because they've given it this high positioning, it simply assumes this high positioning. This is the spirit that makes the impossible suddenly become possible, and as I jerk and shake and as the crowd's roar continues to charge the night, I realize I could use this collective enthusiasm to fuel me for another 50 miles and probably never tire.

We go and go and go; the song looped and eternal, the blur of color in the stands changing tones depending on what camarote we're passing. The spirit of the spectators never wanes nor does ours. Sweat flying off everyone. Tangled costumes. People no longer move along in even rows but instead jump all over the map like a chessboard. When we finally reach the end the music's volume begins to taper. We pass the final edge of the bleachers and go into an end zone where the cleverest of the drink-sellers prey upon our thirsts. Water and beer are guzzled as people rip themselves out of their restrictive, suffocating costumes. Much energy when the *batterias* (samba drummers) make their way out at the end; their instruments causing the streets to pulse and vibrate. We see this as our cue for an encore and dance with more gusto than the whole Avenida stint despite the heat, fatigue, sweat puddles, and fact that we're technically backstage and out of the audience's view (like a band having their own little "post-performance" performance after the gig). All the drummers look like Mahatma Ghandi or the Dalai Lama. They have this aura of holiness that has to do with more than just the fact that they're dressed in white. The elder Bahiana stateswomen come out in their ten-feet wide white dresses and weathered but baby-like faces. They are the perfect oedipal vision of Grandmother, if such a thing exists.

The curse of adulthood, I conclude—as the thousands of Mocidade schoolers all shake hips together—is that we need to have purpose, a reason to do things. A kid'll kick around a can for half the day and see it as time well spent. Carnaval parallels this and it becomes most apparent after the music stops and the show finally winds down. There are discarded costumes strewn about the street (dragon's heads, clown's hands, robot's torsos, spiritual leader's faces), tons of empty beer cans and water bottles and sweaty, exhausted people falling asleep on curbs, heads pillowed in forearms—everyone just done, completely spent. It's like an elaborate sandcastle being washed away by the tide at the end of a summer's day at the beach. It took a long time to build, provided a brief, flickering joy, and is then abandoned—though its effects resonate on forever.

NOT RICHARD NIXON BUT SILVIO SANTOS, A WEALTHY ENIGMATIC TV SHOW HOST WHO'S BEEN KIDNAPPED ONCE OR TWICE.

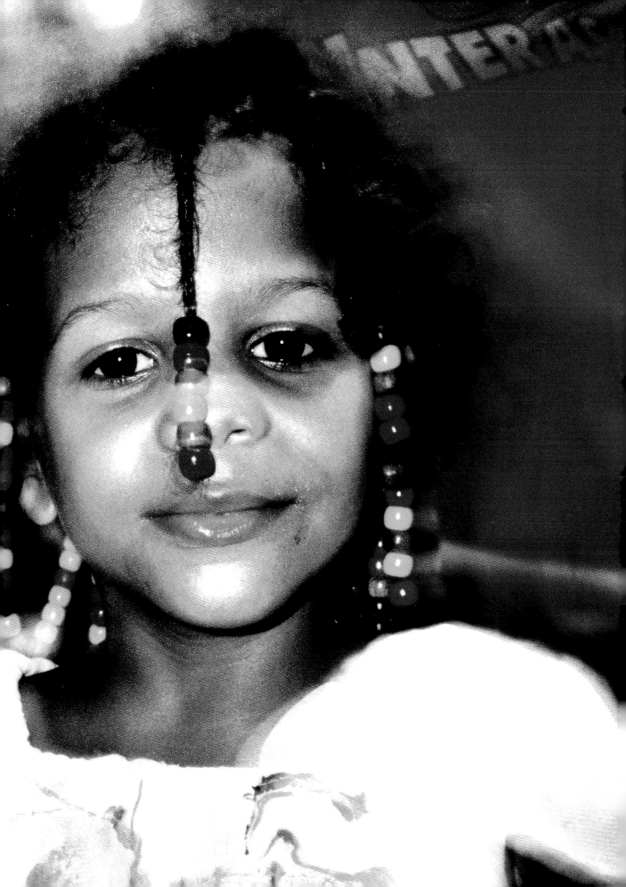

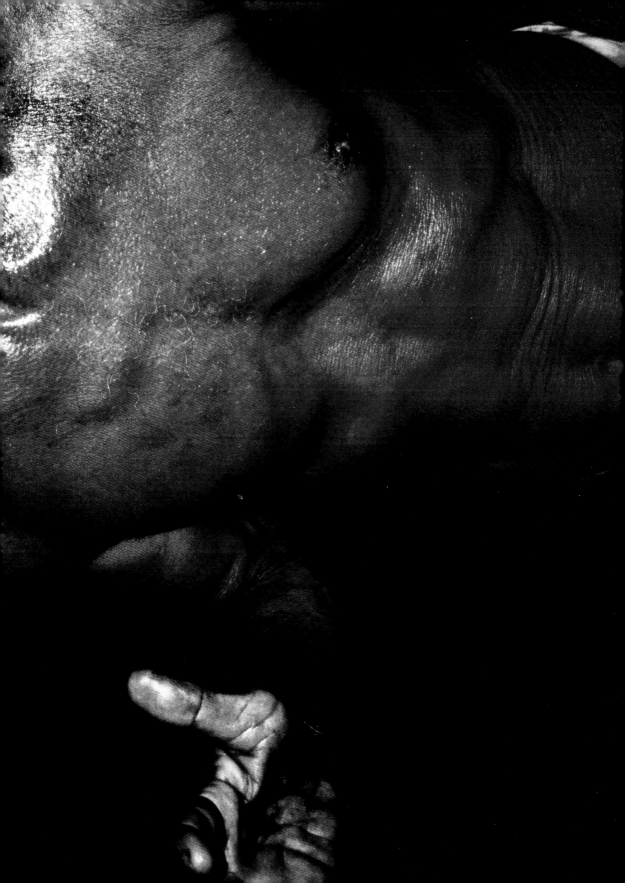

THE UN·IMMACULATE CONCEPTION

When you were conceived, as he was sending his seed up into your mother's ovaries, your biological father was fixated not on your mother but Brigitte Bardot, and so you've spent your entire childhood hinged to an Oedipal connection to lovely Brigitte, though never quite known why. Through high school you get straight A's in French 1, 2, and 3 and go on to get your Masters in French Lit at an ivy league college. As a graduation gift, your father presents to you the Playboy magazine collection he's amassed over the past thirty something years and digging through the stacks, you come across the famous November, 1958 issue where Brigitte appeared in her first nude pictorial (a best-selling issue). You subtract nine months from your birthday and sure enough, come up with November, 1958, the month the Bardot centerspread would've been hovering in the mind of many a married man. You deduce that dad—being the ponderous sort, a quality you too have inherited—must have been more interested in the girl in the magazine than the wife on the bed, and so in much the same way an adopted child goes on the search for his or her biological parents, you go on the quest to find Brigitte, succeed, find out you have more in common with her than your real mother, and ultimately conclude that science is less powerful than sexual imagination.

LOVE IN THE TIME OF MILLENNIAL TENSION

January 1, Year 2000: The shouts of *Bon Année*, the splash of cheap champagne, and the sardine can-warmth of however many thousand people cluttered about the *Rive Droite* as the clock struck twelve were the least memorable things on the big night. The most memorable thing, the thing that will be etched into the mindscapes of all who were fortunate enough to witness it, was the Eiffel Tower looking ready to blast off into the stratosphere like some steel and girder space ship.

It started at the bottom—sparklers fizzing out from the base—and then it climbed, pulling everyone's eyes slowly skyward, a grand salute to man's ability to be occasionally majestic. As the entire tower came into sizzling illumination, a halo of lights entered the picture, circling about the flank the way that famous ring circles Saturn. A moment later it burst at the seams; the phallic symbolism just too obvious to skate around. In an explosion of pent-up tension, fireworks shot out in every direction; the last gasp orgasm of the entire 20th century, the new regime of modern technology on blazing display. There were no bombs, no stock market crashes, no Apocalypse; just an entire world's worth of Y2K paranoia that only served to burst the moment bigger.

Emotions gushed. Tears dripped. It was like some second coming of cyber-Christ had just delivered the news that all would be OK; grandparents cried in the streets, strangers hugged, lovers kissed with more promise than ever before. And the camaraderie and sense of oneness is something I'll never forget. One minute I was slapping high-fives with a fellow American, the next I was kissing cheeks with a lovely Italian girl. To throw this many people out on the streets together and have it all go smooth with no fights, no riots, and no drunken fools stirring up shit is a great feat and sweet commentary on life at the turn of the century.

In the States we don't handle these types of situations so well. In fact a friend told me a story about being at a hunting lodge in Colorodo for New Year's Eve. There was no smoking allowed in this particular establishment but after dinner, a few of the more celebratory gentlemen took it upon themselves to light cigars, being that it was The Big Millennium and all. Well it seems the non-smoking faction didn't take too kindly to this and decided to protest. One thing led to another and the next thing you knew the entire restaurant escalated into a huge fight. Bottles were smashed, chairs were broken, and people were arrested.

On the contrary, an absolutely beautiful moment I saw (and one that would unfortunately be against the law in the U.S.) was a family of five—a mother, a father, a pre-pubescent daughter and a couple of younger sons—sitting on a blanket they had laid out in the middle of the street. The kids and mother held out their champagne glasses while the father tipped the bottle all around. I could see the father's lips moving—some words about the coming year, century, millennium, a sentiment about the good fortune of being at a historical place during a historical time— then the *chin-chin* and the entire family bringing the glasses to their lips. There was all this commotion going on around them yet they somehow created their own private sanctuary right there in the street. It was a snapshot as symbolic of the Millennium spirit as Robert Doisneau's *Kiss at the Hotel d'Ville* is of the romance of Paris.

So what was I doing under the glow of the *Tour Eiffel* on the big night and why am I burdening you with this story? It ties to surfing, actually, or rather, a theory I have about surfing. The dot-com'ers of the world use the word "surfing" to insinuate motion, a continuous changing of the channels. This is a huge compliment but not always true. Some surfers get so locked into their routines they lose sight of the big lesson that's to be learned from riding waves. For surfers to grow they need to leave the beach from time to time, perfumate the nostrils with more than just ocean brine. And just as higher elevation can be felt at ground level, so can surfing be done in landlocked cities. It's just a matter of assuming a mindset of total fluidity, whether the canvas is water or concrete, liquid or cobblestone.

THE TREMENDOUS POWER OF BAD HANDWRITING

Originally, the Eiffel Tower was supposed to be only three-stories high. What eventually happened was Gustave Eiffel, a reputable architect and legendary bridge builder, was commissioned to do the structure by a steel company from Montpellier who were interested in high-profile marketing/advertising.It was not so much about height as it was about interesting architecture. Monsieur Eiffel drew up the blueprints, but just prior to construction, was commissioned a gig he couldn't refuse. In Morocco they needed a 40,000 sq. foot mosque-like abode built for a reknown sultan. The mosque would have spires that shoot to the heavens and all kinds of baroque detail that would make for a great "portfolio piece." Gustav passed the three-story Eiffel Tower on to his interns and headed down to Tangier. He intended to stay six weeks but ended up staying six months, working 14-hour days mostly in fits of crazed, myopic inspiration. As he drove back into Paris half a year later—spent and exhausted, a flask of absinthe at his lap—he could see in the distance this enormous tower, and realized it was positioned right in the vicinity where the three-story steel company structure was to have been built. It was then that he rethought his cryptic scrawling (a technique he developed so no one could rip-off his ideas and one used today by medical doctors worldwide), figured his interns had misinterpreted his blueprints, and what was to be two and a half stories of steel and girder had become instead the highest building the world had ever seen.

ON THE SHORES OF MARSEILLES
A GIANT ORGY OF PEOPLE
GLISTENED ON THE SAND ALL
SHOULDER TO SHOULDER BUT
LIBERATED VIA THE COLLECTIVE.

THERE WERE SKIN TONES
IN TWENTY SHADES OF PINK
+ NOT ENOUGH SUNSCREEN TO GO 'ROUND
BUT THERE WAS SOMETHING
TRANSCENDING IN ALL THE CLUTTER —

A TEMPORARY ESCAPE
FROM THE USUAL HORRORS
OF AN AVERAGE SUNDAY AFTERNOON

during a time of suvan riots
and international surfing contests
i visited tavarua, a tiny island
in fiji most famous for its excellent
waves. there was a sharp contrast
going on. two hours away, at the parl
iament house in suva, was the coup,
the hostages, the mayhem,the
madness. meanwhile, at a surf spot
known as cloudbreak just a short boat
ride from tavarua, there was the
contest--44 of the world's best
surfers battling it out in epic,
ten-foot waves. each afternoon the
competitors would arrive back at
tavarua elated by the great surf and
each night the tv would bring us
late breaking news about hostages
and gunfire. there could have been
a sense of guilt, the feeling that we
were having too good a time while
just an island away all hell was
breaking loose. but there wasnt.
instead there was a sense of
community, a sense of jubilation,
a feeling of GET IT WHILE YA CAN

COUP COUP
IN FIJI

IN THE KINGDOM WE CALL TAVARUA

Though Tavarua is famous for its pristine left-handers—the machine-like precision of Restaurants ("Only the surfer can screw it up, the wave is always perfect," as American Rob Machado pointed out one poolside afternoon) and the barreling beefiness of Cloudbreak—there is indeed a right, and when the elements come together, a damn good one at that.

On Thursday mid-morning, while Restaurants was packed with a good chunk of the Top 44 and Cloudbreak was under scrutiny by contest director Rod Brooks, I paddled out to this righthander, seeing that there were only two people out and it looked overhead and lined-up in a racecourse, speedbarrel kind of way.

The water here is like a bath, not a hot one but one that's right in synch with your body temperature; you feel comfortable and cradled by it. It's clear like a bath too; the bottom is as visible as the side of the road out of a car window and the reef... The reef, for all practical purposes, is like a garden planted by an eccentric grandmother with too much time on her hands and a weakness for five-martini lunches.

There are all kinds of colors, shapes, textures, deep crevices, mushroom heads and random fish fluttering about like aquatic, fluorescent butterflies. The reef is a spectacle, something that would engage the hell out of you if presented on the Discovery channel with all the fascinating facts and tidbits, only I can't recount any of these, I was most interested in catching a wave.

The paddle-out took a good ten minutes (that ring of reef around the island that's so popular in this region of the Pacific) and once I reached the place where the whitewater begins, I realized I'd be sharing waves with Toby and Fletcher, two fine blokes from Australia. Tob and Fletch were cheerful the way surfers are accustomed to being cheerful in a South Pacific line-up full of racy barrels and only three guys out. I saw Toby take-off and pull into the tube with a stalling right hand buried deep in the crystal water. As he passed I duckdove, and with my eyes open I saw the coral, the curl of the wave, a forearm, bottom of board and fin, and thought to myself 'This is more than an apple-less garden, this is a kingdom ruled by bloody Neptune himself.'

"Bloody good stuff out here, matey," yelled Fletcher, as the waves continued.

Fletch caught the next one. It was well overhead and a blank canvas, not as cylindrical as Toby's but playful (if waves are women then this one was a tomboy). He came off the bottom in a style that was markedly "Victorian." The stance slightly narrower, arms very elegant—it's a style that translates well to big waves, which is something the southwest Victorian coast of Australia certainly has, along with cold water, which might've accounted for the huge smile he wore on his face as he carved through the 70 something degree water.

From where I sat, Tavarua resembled Gilligan's Island. It's small and round and packed with palm trees. It has an oasis, slightly unreal quality and from what I'm told, it's shaped like a heart (though you can only see this from the air). Now an "obvious" tourist brochure might market the place as an island of love, and they wouldn't be wrong, but the truth of the matter is this region of ocean is as close to a man-made wavepark as God or whoever's responsible has ever created. There are islands everywhere you look, with no distinct horizon line. Nearby is Namotu which is, of course, wave-infested as well, and then there are other islands, all framed in whitewater...

A wave came. I paddled into it and was almost thrown off by how transparent the water was. I could watch my shadow move across the reef like some alter ego bottom-feeder. The lip was friendly and forgiving and all floaters felt as if they were in slow motion, time suspended the way it is in the barrel. It reeled along doing this strange doubling and tripling up that usually means tube time, but here on the right-hand reef that makes Tavarua ambidextrous, it wasn't a barrel but a schwackfest instead. Five top-turns later I kicked out, hooting to the heavens.

The session continued like this. Fun waves, not epic or world-class, but fun nonetheless with ten minute or so intervals that were pretty much welcomed by Toby, Fletcher and myself as opportunities to marvel at just how blue the sky is, how green the islands are, how clear and warm the water is, and just how damn good it is to be a surfer here in the Pacific Ocean between the equator and the Tropic of Capricorn, just east of euphoria and a hair west of Nirvana.

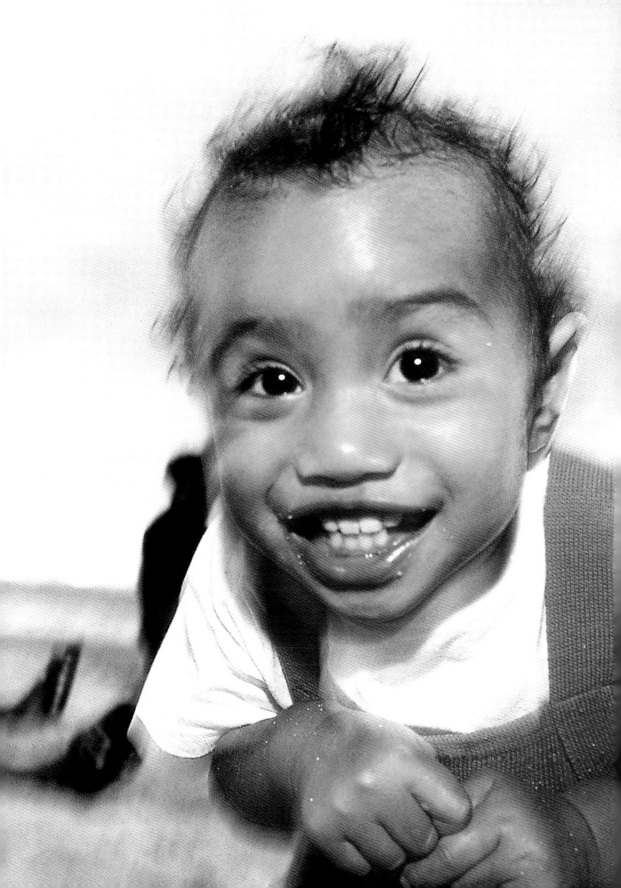

SEA SNAKES, CONCH SHELLS, AND SHINY, HAPPY FIJIANS (BUT NO SIGN OF HOLLYWOOD REDHEADS)

On a lazy, almost-waveless day I decided to do the circular stroll around the tiny island we call Tavarua. Here's what it looked like:

From the Restaurants side you look across a knee-deep shelf that stretches about a quarter mile to a shimmering band of whitewater. In the midday sun, this inner reef—the shelf between the shoreline and where the waves break—is illuminated by tiger stripes of refracted light. They flicker with the current, moving about in constant flux. You really can't tell whether this dance is thousands of independent tentacles or maybe just one giant, interconnected web... and the trying to figure it out is what keeps the eyes fixed.

Out beyond the whitewater the ocean turns to a richer, deeper blue which, of course, it literally is. Popcorn clouds cling to the horizon line and the sun's reflection off the surface is blinding. Looking islandward, Tavarua's interior is nothing but trees and shrubbery; very dense, with about a hundred feet of sand outlining it.

From the air this entire package looks like a nucleus of rich green, and around it a sand-colored ring, a turquoise inner-reef ring, a bright band of whitewater, and then a dark Pacific stretching to eternity i.e. the horizon line. Metaphorically speaking, the nucleus of Tavarua could be the womb and these bands the various stages of a native's life (breast-feeding in the green, learning to swim in the turquoise, learning to surf where the whitewater is, going fishing i.e. manhood out in the deep blue... What I can't figure out is whether the afterlife is represented by the horizon line or the sky? But anything other than the moment at hand seems a long, long way away, especially with the life-sustaining sun beating on my back).

Further along I come across a track; not the sole of a pair of Nikes or Adidas from one of the surfers, but a snake track—a sea snake track. I follow it about five paces and sure enough: the snake itself. It's about two-and-a-half feet long, silvery with black rings and a head that goes slightly yellow. It's slithering toward the shade of the trees. They say they're harmless, that they can only wrap their mouths around the webs between our fingers or toes. I say that's all fine and dandy, I'm still not going too close.

I keep walking till I arrive at the small curve in the island that gives Tavarua its heart shape. It's actually a tiny bay you could almost throw a football across. Because of its deeper water, this is where the motorboats and jetskis launch. This is also where surfboards are kept (in the shade, under a thatched roof, of course).

The entire Tavaruan water patrol is out this morning—gassing up the skis, checking the tides, preparing for yet another day of taking people surfing, fishing, and the like. There's the Phoenician belief that time spent on the water is not deducted from one's life. If this is truly the case then these people's immortality might be bigger than Elvis Presley's; and where Elvis's is in a symbolic, "living legend" sort of way, these people's—assuming the Phoenicians are correct—would be very literal. So if you show up here in thirty years and come across a twenty year old-looking gent who claims to be eighty-four…well, you get the picture.

I chat with the boatmen. They're seemingly very, very happy and at peace with the world. Their smiles seem as natural as the blinking of eyes. Maybe this is because of the fact that life is low in anxieties and stress on this little oasis of an island. Maybe it's because there are no cars or traffic. It could also have to do with the fact that three times a day, a plump, serene-faced lady blows on a conch shell to summon the entire camp to the restaurant for breakfast, lunch and dinner. The baritone sound of the shell comes across as maternal; whether this is because of its pitch or because we associate dinner calls with Mom, I don't know. What I do know is that I'm hungry, and as quickly as I think this, sure enough, there's that sound. So it's with this that our circle island tour comes to an end. Tavarua has a "time standing still" quality about it. Wearing a watch would be blasphemous and discordant. The fact that my little midday walk took about two hours but could've been done in fifteen minutes is of no concern. To measure it in footsteps rather than time seems a lot more appropriate. I intended to do this, but lost count somewhere around one hundred and forty-seven.

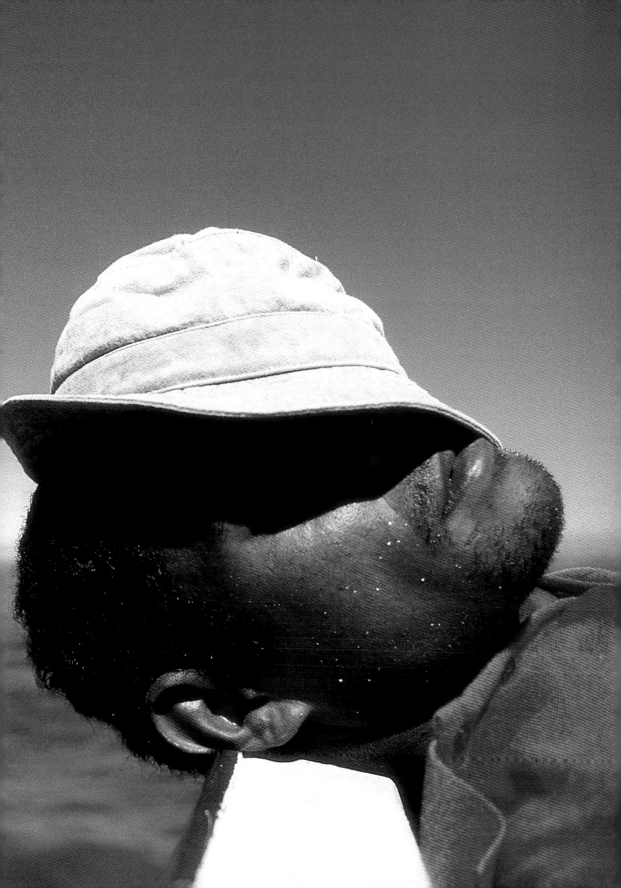

THE ONLY DIFFERENCE BETWEEN PIGS IN A BLANKET AND EGGS ON A PLATE IS ONE STANDS THE RISK OF BEING CAUGHT IN A ZIPPER WHILE THE OTHER IS ENHANCED BY TABASCO SAUCE THE ONLY DIFFERENCE BETWEEN MAN AND GOD IS MAN THINKS AND GOD KNOWS THE ONLY DIFFERENCE BETWEEN HARRY AND A HOMOSEXUAL PLUMBER IS THAT HARRY DON'T WORK FOR ROTO.ROOTER THE ONLY DIFFERENCE BETWEEN VINCENT VAN GOGH AND MYSELF IS WHERE VINNIE WOULD GO FOR AN EAR I GENERALLY GRAVITATE TOWARD AN INDEX FINGER THE ONLY DIFFERENCE BETWEEN THINGS BEING NOT QUITE RIGHT AND THINGS BEING PERFECT IS A SUBTLE SHIFT IN THE CEREBRAL CORTEX THE ONLY DIFFERENCE BETWEEN VOICE MAIL AND ROBOTS AT STARBUCKS IS VOICEMAIL OFFERS NO DECAF THE ONLY DIFFERENCE BETWEEN THE FLAMING LIPS OF A YOUNG BRASILIAN GIRL AND THE BLAZING EYES OF AN OLD INDIAN GURU IS

ONE REQUIRES PYROTECHNICS WHILE THE OTHER INVOLVES SIMPLY RUBBING TWO PIECES OF WOOD TOGETHER THE ONLY DIFFERENCE BETWEEN THE LATE NIGHT URGES OF PAMELA ANDERSON AND THE EARLY MORNING DEMANDS OF NAOMI CAMPBELL IS ONE REQUIRES CARROTS WHILE THE OTHER CALLS FOR CUCUMBERS THE ONLY DIFFERENCE BETWEEN COLON-IZING MARS & RESIDING IN ORANGE COUNTY IS ONE'S MORE IN NEED OF AN ENEMA THAN THE OTHER THE ONLY DIFFERENCE BETWEEN GOING TO YOUR ANSWERING MACHINE EXPECTING A SINGLE MESSAGE THAT'LL CHANGE YOUR LIFE FOREVER & GOING TO CHURCH ON SUNDAY IS ONE SEEKS TO FIND GOD IN A FORMAL WAY WHILE THE OTHER SEEKS TO CREATE THE CREATOR IN AN IMAGE OF HIS I HER OWN MAKING THE ONLY DIFFERENCE BETWEEN HER ENERGY PRE·BREAK UP & HER ENERGY POST·BREAK UP IS BEFORE SHE WAS LIKE A SHIRLEY TEMPLE BUT NOW SHE'S MERELY A SEVEN·UP

Aplomb, whose sexual fantasy is to fall out of a plane at 5,000 feet and land perfectly on a flat-on-his-back, erect man's penis and experience orgasm in unison in that millisecond before the big squash, said to Genevieve, a friend who seeks not the sick and the twisted, but the loving and synchronized: "All this talk about thumb tacks… Makes a girl want to take up motorcycles or something. Something with a serious hum and shake to it." There are legions of love-starved S&Mers in the suburbs, only most of their desires are uncomplicated not because their minds lack imagination but because their loins have no vocabulary. If love and sex were to sit down to a long cup of tea, they'd jointly conclude that all paths lead back to the missionary position, full eye contact, and

I love you at the point of orgasm.

1,000 LOINS RAISED HIGH IN THE THROES OF ECSTASY

While airplanes prefer smooth, straight, unobstructed landing strips, orgasms, on the other hand, thrive on curves and lips and hips and textures and shadows...

Simon, slouched at the bar all melancholic and euphoric, rationalized his drinking problem as follows: *My mother plucked me from the nipple a day too soon, hence my life has been riddled in unquenchable thirst.* "Bartender!" he demanded, a fist pounding the table. "'Nuther gin and tonic."

Question: Where's Tom and his girlfriend?
Answer: Well they're in one of two places. They're either on some secluded beach somewhere sharing waves and lapping up the sun or...they're locked in the bedroom going for the fifth or six orgasm of the day...They're digging deep. The sheets are scattered and the mattress has shaken its way across the room. Cigarettes have been smoked and wine bottles have been emptied. Their entire hash supply has been exhausted and their primary form of lubrication is sunscreen.

Guy walks into a women's boutique, says "My mother's turning 58 tomorrow, what do I get her?" Woman behind the counter pulls out a handbag with red and pink swirls. "This is Pucci," she says. "Perfect," says the guy. "When my mother lost her virginity...to my father, *after they were married* of course—she was wearing a Pucci dress. "We also have them in green," says the girl. "No," says the guy. "No, the red is perfect."

THIRST QUENCHED (THE END OF BOOZING BUT THE EARLY STAGES OF SADISM): Kissing her tears away, Simon developed a taste for the salty emotion, and realized that unlike sea water, the salt in tears doesn't fight with digestion. This was water, water everywhere and absolutely perfect to drink.

She lay sprawled on the couch—the phone up to her ear, the cigarette up to her mouth—"Do you miss me?" she asked in a vulnerable tone. He looked across the empty room—there was no furniture, no stereo, and nothing on the walls. "I miss some form of tranquility that you have yet to become the poster child for" he thought, but by the time it got to his lips sounded like, "Yes...Yes I miss you."

"Let's get drunk and kill god!"
–proposal from Thunder Burns, an 11-year old BB gun owner who leads the weekly "gang" meetings held late at night in Bobby Greenfield's backyard treefort.

Danny blamed his nervous breakdown on the constant turnover of new shoes. "It was like I was at the batting cages," he told his psychiatrist, "and then the machine went into overdrive. Balls started coming at me faster and faster and faster..." He leaned forward in his chair and crossed his legs, a red pair of Diesel joggers glistened in the windowlight. They looked brand new, but in fact they were last week's model. "I tried to keep up...but now I just can't play that game."

In response to a friend saying he met a girl in a supermarket who will one day be his wife:
"And when you finally do consummate the relationship, for God's sake shoot for children! Don't sit on the fence and don't dabble in birth control devices for the first six months to be "sure" about things. This is where all the uncertainty in the world comes from. If every couple went into their first lovemaking session with the intention of procreation, their kids would inherit this sense of total conviction, and we'd have a globe full of people who know exactly why they're here."

It was in the brief battery life of his Macintosh laptop that Leroy came to fully understand the frustrations women have with short-wicked men.

She curled up to her dolly, looked at it as if it were human. "How come the love I want to feel exists only in song lyrics?" she asked, though the doll—a Barbie clad in a pink bikini—gave no reply.

"I look for love in the eyes of every hand that reaches out to me...don't matter if it's just some waitress passing me my pepperoni pizza."
—Rodney Altomare, frequent Italian restaurant patron

"I have more love in my heart than an eleven-year-old schoolgirl at lunchtime"
—Oscar Herrera, janitor

Gazing into the back of his new lover who was fast asleep, Winston saw a constellation of freckles and a universe of possibility. He saw Venus and Jupiter and Saturn and Pluto. He eventually saw the Milky Way and one thing led to another...

"What is the name of the bouillabaisse that mixes bedknobs and broomsticks and why must love be found at the bottom of this concoction?"
—Dr. Robert Reesman, cardiologist

Two love-starved men stand on the corner, cups of coffee in their hands. "About thirty seconds..." the one says as a rosy-cheeked, long-legged woman walks by. "What are you talking about?" asks the other. "It would take me about thirty seconds to fall in love with her," he clarifies, the sound of high heels on pavement fading, the coffee only getting colder.

"We Embrace Sinners and Whoares Alike at the Church of the Kicked Open Door"
—graffiti scrawled on the Williamsburg Bridge

An observation from a frequent flyer after running into a dear and distant friend in an airport:
An incredible shrinking world. One decade the size of a basketball, the next a tennis ball, the next a small marble you can fit in your pocket and clench firmly in the palm of your hand.

"You kiddin' me...I'm like some perverse uncle who waits for some 10-year-off-in-the-distance future when the legs part and the heart and mouth open wide and the gills spread their buttery wings..."
—Obese, hairy Brooklynite subway rider whose favorite book is *100 Love Sonnets* by Pablo Neruda

A question for Mr. President:
Is there an inconsistency in the way we'll electric chair a serial killer and assume him eradicated from the face of the planet yet when a nice person dies we'll say he or she "lives on in the hearts of all of us?"

A question for conductors of rebirthing processes:
Would a child conceived in an elevator be less likely to suffer motion sickness? Would a kid conceived in a punk rock slam pit be more comfortable around strange, sweaty bodies?

A question for western doctors:
What's better to eat? Chocolate ice cream with gooey swirls of marshmallow and caramel made by a family-run company who donate a share of the profits to environmental efforts...or miso soup, lentils, brown rice, grilled fish on a bed of organic greens, all to be washed down with a glass of carrot juice prepared for you by one Mr. Richard Ramirez, serial killer, who overcharges you for the meal and uses the money to extend his basement torture chamber

A question for carnivores:
Is the vegetarian who points his or her finger at the person who has *fois gras*, venison, and veal on New Year's Eve...is that vegetarian still technically a vegetarian if, on the way home from the party, he or she accidentally runs over a rabbit?

A question for those prone to bumber stickers:
Is the pro-lifer who manslaughters a pro-choicer in front of the abortion clinic still a pro-lifer?

we were pretenders pretending
to be masqueraders
at a halloween party
for false pretentious hollywood types
(we felt terribly underdressed)
i looked at you
you looked away from me
and our future arrived
light as a hummingbird
pouncing on a piece of rye bread
that would turn to a wad of mildew
come wintertime

we were confined to the missionary position
before the chiropractor referred
us to the acupuncturist who
worked her white magic
from there we found new positions
which later became new languages
of which the world would soon embrace

we were disorderly but far from drunk
the last i saw you
a hyper-real goodbye fell from your lips
a phosphorescent smoke
shooting from your tailpipe
as you attempted to drive away
but later overheated and broke down
on a highway
reduced to one lane
on account of 'reconstruction'

we were 12-steppers side-stepping
the real issue
that cause, symptom, and simple
'cursed-at-birth' destiny
could not be confined to a meeting
involving coffee, confessions,
and more tattoos
than the sturges sessions the
harley-davidson people
seem to flock to each year

we were lovers back in 1974
though it's all probably a blur to you now
or rather a smear
on some bedsheet buried
at the bottom of your closet

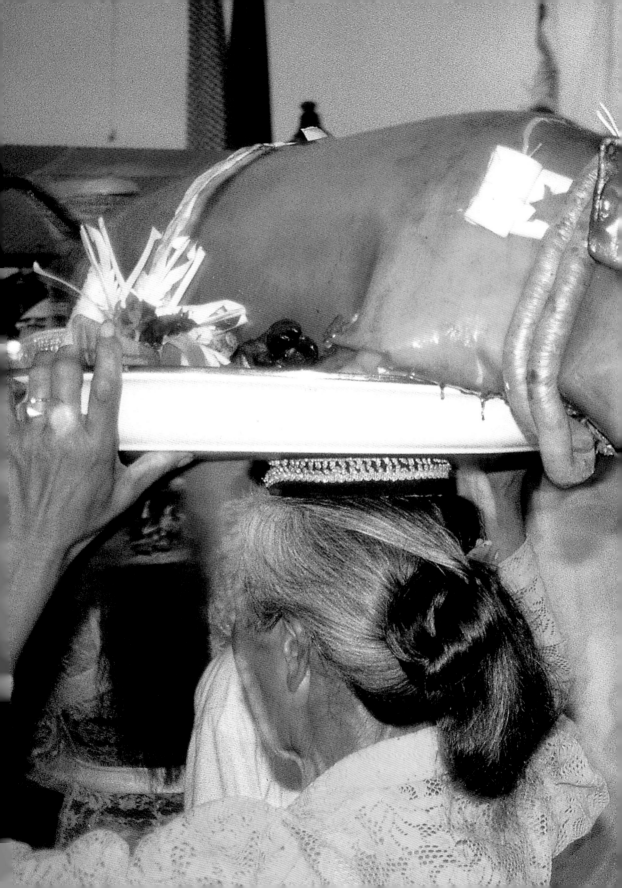

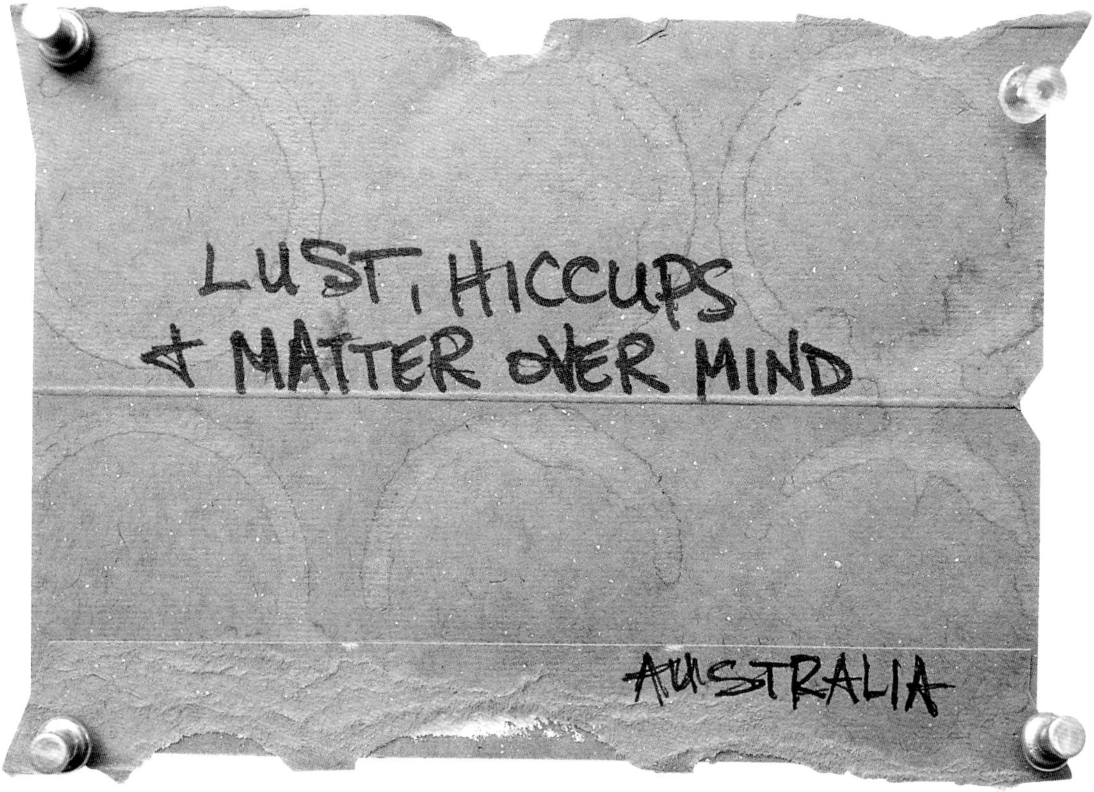
LUST, HICCUPS
& MATTER OVER MIND
AUSTRALIA

A HICCUP IN HIS MACHO ARMOR
or THE THINGS WE DO FOR LUST
or ~~MIND OVER MATTER~~
MATTER OVER MIND

There were sixteen empty Cooper's bottles on the table when Chops and Parko got up to make their way for the door at Metropolis, a trendy, yuppified nightclub in the financial district of Sydney. Cooper's is the strongest bottle in the business, the true Ocker brew, and the two blokes took snide pleasure in knocking them back at a place that was more likely to serve neat martinis to extremely neat suit and tie types. Chops wore a sarcastic, Sid Vicious snarl on his face; the only reason he was even at such a swanky club was because the *Adrenaline* Awards Night was on, and with Chops being one of the top skateboarders in the world, and *Adrenaline* being the top skate rag in Australia, it was more or less mandatory that he attend.

In his burgundy Doc Marten boots, skin-tight, skin-head-esque torn-up jeans, black leather jacket with white Anarchy "A" stenciled across the back, and blonde four-inch high mohawk, Chops was, needless to say, way out of place. He and sidekick/lookalike Parko pushed their way through the self-conscious dancing folk and exited out the entryway, passing the muscled doorman and out the velvet rope. On Walker Street they hailed a taxi—or rather, cut to the front of the queue to hail a taxi—and directed the Vietnamese driver toward King's Cross.

Chops was the cliched image of the rebel punk; he was tattooed from head to toe, used "fuck" in just about every sentence, and took great pride in his beer belly and bad teeth. His skateboarding style was an extension of all this—fearless and reckless and masochistic. He held the record for most broken bones (twenty-one at last count) yet somehow the injuries never slowed him down. There was always something a little forced about his macho act, however, and the fact that he came from upper middle class, loving parents who were still happily married made one wonder where all the anger came from.

Parko, on the other hand, was a far gentler version of Chops. He wore the garb, sported the ink, and knocked back the piss but was all in all a sweet, pimply-faced kid.

Across the Sydney Harbour Bridge the city lights fizzed and wobbled; the landmark opera house luminous and elegant and at polar opposites with the seedy place where the boys were headed. King's Cross is were hookers, junkies, yobbos, dirty dole bludgers and pretty much all stripe of the down-and-out congregate.

Heading up William Street, the main artery into the Cross, Chops's eyes found themselves fixated on the transvestites that worked the left side of the street while Parko's stared into the giant, luminous Coca-Cola sign straight ahead which, far as where Parko's head was at, may as well have read "Cocaine." The two punks jumped out of the cab in front of The Bourbon and Beefsteak where they went in and abruptly took to knocking back four or five Jack and Cokes in quick succession. The real coke—speed actually, though they only found this out after the deal was done—came a couple hours later.

Parko had been hit up by a pasty-skinned, gaunt-faced dealer on a neighboring barstool. He borrowed a wad of cash from Chops and followed this guy out the door and down a narrow passageway between an X-rated movie house and a pub called The Launch Pad. The smell of urine and vomit rose from the pavement. A $50 note left Parko's hand and a baggie full of powder replaced it. Minutes later the boys were chopping up lines in a toilet stall and snorting the stuff through a sloppily rolled $20 bill.

Drunk and supercharged. The way they liked it. The next place they hit was Kiddy O'Shea's where there was more booze, more unraveling of the senses, less caution and far less consciousness. At this point the two were running on autopilot. At this point they also lost each other. Chops had gotten up to take a piss and never came back.

A couple drinks later, Parko—teeth grinding and palms sweating—decided it was time to call it a night. The sun was just coming up as he hailed a cab and made his way back to the hotel they were staying at in Bondi Junction. A couple hours later, when Parko had just managed to fidget himself to sleep, the phone rang. It was Chops's father.

"Chops is in intensive care," he said in a frightening tone. "He's been viciously stabbed and sliced up."

The story goes that Chops walked into the wrong toilet in the wrong pub at the wrong time. His abdomen had a deep gouge and the inside of his left hand was a stutter of gashes. It wasn't until a day later that Chops was conscious enough to tell what exactly had happened. Apparently he'd innocently walked into the men's room for a piss when he came across two very stunned, very evil faces. One of them was holding a large chunk of cash while the other was holding a fat bag of white powder. A speed deal, a very serious one; so serious, in fact, that the dealer, the one holding the cash, decided it'd be best to quickly exterminate the witness. He pulled a switchblade from his pocket and stuck it straight into Chops, just below the belly button. There was a cold burst of adrenaline, a shock that would make most men crumble at the knees. But Chops wasn't most men—he was Chops The Bad Arse—and when the speed dealer attempted to bring the knife upward in a fatal gutting, Chops grabbed the blade with both hands, pushed downward, and let out a baritone roar that sent both men fleeing out the back window, and ultimately saved his life.

The skate mags featured stories about the stabbing. There were photos of Chops all bandaged up in his hospital bed, "Wrong place, wrong time" headlines; it was a horrific nightmare that thankfully ended on a good note.

A month or so later Chops was back in action; flashing his irreverent grin and happily showing off his new scars. The stabbing man, incidentally, was never caught.

But it wasn't until a decade later that the real story came out, and it was more a read-between-the-lines thing than a direct confession. At a halfpipe in Bronte I ran into a couple of Chops's former mates and asked after him. "Haven't you heard?" they replied as though the latest on Chops was common knowledge. A year so after the stabbing, it turns out, Chops had moved on from the skate scene and stopped hanging out in those circles. He'd quit skateboarding altogether, bought a flat in Paddington, put on thirty or forty lbs. and only recently came out of the closet. And though he's no longer a skate god but instead an assistant chef at a local cafe, and though he's massively beer-bellied and terrifically out of shape, and though he hasn't spoken to his parents in over a year and half, Chops has never been better in his whole entire life.

So you see, there was no speed deal that he'd unluckily walked in on after all. There were, however, a lot of repressed desires that unraveled at the end of a sauced-up, drug-fucked evening. There was a clumsy, slit-eyed piss against a tightly-wedged urinal where a handsome man happened to be doing the same business only a foot or two away. There was a turning of the head that happened without volition, a gaze that met the other man's mid-section, and then a dropping of the lower jaw and a reflexive reach for this man's cock. And then there were probably words and then a knife and then instant sobriety on Chops's part, and an ambulance and an I.V. and a story that saved his reputation and credibility in the skate scene.

But what's most fucked up is the reaction of the pursued man. A mean looking, drunken punk makes a move for your heterosexual cock in a restroom where there's no one else around. You may be deeply offended, you may want to punch him, you may even want to ram his head in the fucking toilet...but do you want to kill him? Maybe if you somehow believe you invited the gesture, that you yourself were giving off something that said, "I'm wide open." But then there's little ration and reason in a men's toilet in the sleaziest, most hopeless pub in all of King's Cross at 5:30 AM on a Friday night. Ask the poor bastard who gets stuck cleaning the toilets on Saturday mornings. He'll tell you there's not a lot of focus, not a lot of aim...things just sort of go wherever they go.

THEY CALL IT
THE SPORT OF KINGS

DUKE'S CANOE CLUB
WAIKIKI

PIPELINE, NORTH SHORE, HAWAII

SPAWNED FROM THE ANKLE-SLAPPING SURF OF WEST FLORIDA, CORY LOPEZ IS FAMOUS FOR ATTEMPTING TO RIDE ONE OF THE MEANEST, THICKEST, NASTIEST WAVES THE WORLD HAS EVER SEEN. IT WAS AT A SPOT CALLED TEAHUPO'O AND THE WAVE WAS MORE LIKE A SEA MONSTER THAN SOMETHING YOU'D ATTEMPT TO SURF. HE DROPPED DOWN THE FACE AND PULLED INTO A TUBE THE SIZE OF A BANQUET ROOM IN A 5-STAR HOTEL, EXCEPT IN THIS CASE WATER WASN'T SERVED IN GLASSES BUT MORE LIKE BIBLICAL FLOOD. THE WAVE EXPLODED, RIPPED CORY FROM HIS BOARD, PULLED HIM DOWN FOR WHAT SEEMED LIKE AN ETER- NITY, AND THEN SHOT HIM TO THE SURFACE WITH A NEW AND IMPROVED GLOW IN HIS EYES.

FLAVIO PADARATZ IS BRASIL'S #1 SURFER. HIS WAVE-RIDING IS SUPER-CHARGED AND HIS PERSONALITY IS SUPER ENTHUSIASTIC. HE LIVES IN SANTA CATARINA IN THE SOUTH & LISTENS TO SAMBA, TROPICALIA, & BOSSA NOVA. HE ALSO PLAYS DRUMS IN A BAND & PRACTICES YOGA ON A DAILY BASIS. "I'M EXPLORING THE POWER OF MY BRAIN," HE SAYS OF HIS YOGA FETISH/MEDITATION FASCINATION. "ALL MY POWER COMES FROM MY THINKING SO I WANT TO MAKE IT AS STRONG AS I POSSIBLY CAN... THERE'S REALLY NO LIMIT."

THE ULTRA · AMNIOTIC

Veronica Kay is an international model/pro surfer who's dovetailed the two vocations into one. She walks runways and waltzes across waves with equal grace; she knows the glamour of flashbulbs as well as the glory of getting tubed. Of the baptismal qualities of surfing she says, "It puts things in perspective... Even if you just jump in the ocean and get out right away you feel a hundred times better." Of the benefits of being in the public eye, she says nothing.

"I have pondered the ceilings of the Sistine Chapel, I've marveled at the Pyramids, I've stuttered in the presence of kings and queens and gods and ghosts, I have watched a Sevillan bullfighter stick his farpa into a bull the size of an elephant and seen the blood glow chocolate brown in the dirt...Your beauty and grace, dear Veronica, surpasses all these things. Join me on a road trip to Florida. We'll drink Cosmopolitans in the sun shine, and fall in love come November." —letter from a fan called "Willy" (sent over the Internet)

TO MOVE MOUNTAINS + MANIPULATE TIME

In December of 1987, during an eight-to-ten foot swell on the North Shore of Oahu, Tom Carroll had one of those surfs that makes you feel like you can move mountains. The next morning he would be competing in the finals of the Pipeline Masters and there was no doubt in his mind that victory lay fatefully in the palm of his hand. That is until the phone rang. Tom was informed that his older sister had just been killed in a car wreck. It was a ton of bricks, a dose of kryptonite, a moment you know at the time that it's happening will change your life forever. Most would've cracked. Tom, instead, quarantined himself in his hotel, didn't tell anyone of the news, and more or less postponed the inevitable. The following day he walked solemnly down to the contest, put on his jersey, paddled out, and proceeded to unleash every bit of unfairness in the world on the fifteen foot faces of Pipeline. It was a mind-boggling performance that left many onlookers scratching their heads and rethinking the laws of gravity. When they announced him the victor in front of a beachful of applauding fans, there was no verbal dedication, only a shutting of the eyes and a clenching of the fists and a bouncing back and forth between two extremes of emotion that only Tom could begin to describe.

IN SAMOA, ON A TRIP
WHERE SURFING AND
MUSIC BLURRED
BORDERS AND FED
INTO EACH OTHER
THE WAY THE LINES
OF AN INFINITY SYMBOL
DO, PERRY FARRELL
WAS A BUNDLE OF
RAMPANT ENTHUSIASM.
HE RODE WAVES WITH
RHYTHMS IN HIS HEAD
AND WROTE SONGS WITH
SALTWATER DRIPPING
FROM HIS PEN. PERRY'S
LOVE OF SURFING IS
NOT SOME HYPED-UP
BULLSHIT DEVISED TO
MAKE ITS WAY ONTO
PRESS RELEASES. HE'S
A GENUINE CHARGER.
I WATCHED HIM TAKE OFF
ON A 10-FOOT WAVE &
HOLD A HIGH LINE WITH
THE SAME BOLDNESS HE
HOLDS ONSTAGE. AT
NIGHT, WITH RECORDING
EQUIPMENT SET UP IN
HIS HOTEL ROOM, HE'D
DRAW FROM THE ENDORPHIN
RELEASE OF THE SURFING
AND POUR IT INTO VOCAL
TRACKS. A BEAUTIFUL
PROCESS TO WATCH, A
LITTLE LIKE ALCHEMY.

FLIGHT FROM THE FAVELA
NAME: MAGNEO
AGE: 9
HOME: FAVELA CANTAGALO,
     RIO DE JANEIRO,
     BRASIL
MISSION: TO USE SURFING
     AS HIS SPRINGBOARD
     OUT OF THE GHETTO.
     TO BECOME CHAMPION
     OF THE WORLD AND
     TO UTILIZE HIS STATURE
     TO HELP OTHER
     FAVELA KIDS.

"IT FELT LIKE GOD WAS PUSHING ME UP
FROM BEHIND"
   —EVAN WRIGHT (BLIND SURFER),
REMEMBERING WHAT IT WAS LIKE TO
CATCH HIS FIRST WAVE

JUSTIN'S WEIRD ACT

He sanded the ding with 80-grit paper, as he'd done a hundred times before, masking taped off the damaged area, as he'd done a hundred times before, and proceeded to mix first the resin and then the hardener in a disposable plastic cup, as he'd done a hundred times before. Only this time a glob of catalyst had crusted over the pour spout, and so instead of dripping out the exit hole, the catalyst burst through the seam at the bottom of the squirt, a white flash that landed square in Justin's eyes.

There were screams. There was a phone call to the paramedics. There was a shower in which the water shot out at full blast and Justin pried each eye open the way we pry open difficult crustaceans at mealtime, only this was no feast, this was a major fiasco, a fiasco that ended up costing Justin his sight.

Blinded. From a clumsy attempt at a stupid ding repair. It was a hard one to swallow, and after eleven years of rigorous surfing, it was one that would quite literally stay with him forever.

Justin's surfing days began on the southeast coast not far from Ulladullah. His older brothers got him into it, and from the first wave he stood up on at Bendalong Beach at the age of 12, he was signed up for life. But what separated Justin's surfing experience from most was that he was into isolation. He didn't like sharing waves, line-ups, roof racks, rides to the beach. He didn't even like sharing sand, and this had less to do with selfishness than it did the fact that for him, surfing was about communion with nature, not his fellow man. He was a purist. He felt that surfing was trapped by the very conventions it initially sought to escape—conformity, capitalism, competitiveness—and that most of surfers had missed the point altogether.

"When I paddle out it's 'cause I want to enjoy the ocean—its peace, its serenity…and not to have it poisoned by some guy bobbing about in the line-up next to me," he used to say.

Throughout high school he'd sneak off in the afternoons to his secret backbeach. It involved a fifteen-minute hike through the bush and then a long walk along the shoreline. The sand didn't squeak, he pointed out more than once, it squealed, and Justin likened this to the fact his spot was untapped, virginlike.

In the two years he'd been surfing there he'd never come across a single waverider, be it a boardsurfer, bodysurfer, waveskier, or boogieboarder. When you take into account how bad the wave was, this was no mystery. The bank seemed to run on a never changing, direct parallel line with the shore, and consequently, the wave was a complete closeout. From the grassy north headland to the rocky outcropping to the south, a stretch of about a kilometer and a half, one long wall of water would curl over at exactly the same time, blatantly defying the term "surfable coastline." But Justin didn't mind. This was where the imagination came in, he'd say optimistically. This was where the challenge lie.

Justin's approach was an odd one. First of all, his style was inspired by his background in yoga. A hippie friend had introduced him to it as a kid, and he'd done it every morning for as long as he could remember. When he'd jump to his feet on a wave, he'd immediately check himself, make sure his posture was correct, confirm that his feet were in the right positions. It was a methodical way of going about things, perhaps overly so, and his mates gave him a hard time about it. Justin just laughed. His quest on the waveriding front was exactly that: "wave riding." As he'd said a hundred times before, "High-performance is about harmony and not domination."

They say no two waves are alike, but in the case of Justin's closeout, each one seemed to be exactly like the last, as if created by machine, though in the cruelest possible way. There was time for only one move: a bottom turn/off the top combo, which drove Justin to places no closeout waverider before him had ever gone.

"It's not the one move that makes a great ride," he announced one spring morning at the pie shop. "This would be like peaking in your youth and then just giving up during middle and old age."

It was around this time Justin stopped wearing leggies and began riding every wave to shore. The ride, far as he was concerned, was like an Olympic diver's magnificent somersault-into-jack knife routine. There was the gymnastic bit but there was also the finale. The cutting of the water was a big part of the score, as was his fins cutting into the sand after one of his perfect rides. It was about thoroughness; a fully concentrated performance that began the moment he turned around and stroked for a wave and didn't end until he stepped off on the shore. Which led him to elaborate theories about skateboarders, and the amount of imagination it takes to make the same backyard halfpipe interesting. He thought of his spot in this context, and began referring to his rides as runs. There were yoga postures performed in the white wash—*Adho Mukha* (downward dog), *Bhujangasana* (cobra), and *Bakasana* (crane), handstands, spinners...

His senior year was spent perfecting the standing back flip, what most of us considered to be the most original move we'd ever witnessed.

"All about timing it just as the wave's exploded, that moment where the water's shooting upward instead of forward," he'd explain.

Justin would take off, do a vertical off the lip in the closeout, come down, and kick his feet in the air in front of him, twirling into an absolutely perfect backflip, and then land dead center on his board, bogging a bit with the impact of his weight, but riding onward, all the way to the shore. It was beyond *rad* or *filthy* or *sick*. It was *astonishing, acrobatic*. It was a move that earned you a name like Bobo or Cecile and had a place more in the circus than on the pro surfing circuit. One of us had threatened to get a photographer down to shoot it, we figured the surf mags would be into running a sequence of it for sure. But then Justin wanted no part of this, and so his somersaults were left as a South Coast legend, one that people would talk about in the pub, maybe even knock over someone's pint trying to explain.

So strange that Justin would devote years of his surfing life to a wave that was so utterly predictable, so production line-like, and then later lose his sight and have his entire existence be all about that very thing; predictability, consistency, things being positioned exactly where they're supposed to.

Justin stayed in the hospital a full week after the accident. He'd burnt out his cornea with the toxic catalyst, and the doctors told him it was heads or tails whether they'd grow back properly.

They didn't.

It's been three years. Justin is confined to a walking stick and a pair of dark, blocky sunglasses (he's allergic to dogs). He's quite proficient in Braille and quite prolific in his reading. But his physical life is severely limited, and so there's undoubtedly a lot that gets pent up with no direct outlet, at least not the one we as surfers all know. His spirit however, when it comes to entertaining himself for purely personal reasons, is as resourceful as it was the day he committed himself to mastering a closeout. He finds ways to keep things interesting, one of which, believe it or not, is fingerboarding. He can entertain himself for hours on end going back and forth in an eighteen-inch high halfpipe with a two-inch long skateboard under his fingertips. He does grinds, airs, and one-fingered ballet-style moves that are not unlike the things he'd do when he was surfing.

Justin shares a small flat with his sister Fiona (she takes care of him) which has become a big hangout for the local school kids. He's good to them, inspires in them the desire to be true to themselves, even though most of them are unaware of it. Justin gets a sense of fulfillment from this, a reason to move forward.

Another thing that keeps Justin from putting a gun to his head is his acute attention to his remaining four senses, or more specifically, the dramatic improvements he's made when it comes to smelling, touching, hearing, and tasting. Take this rather odd comment, for example: He'd heard a story about a man getting killed in a car accident, which evidently had been captured on video. What happened was the guy was speaking on his cell phone at a red light that'd just turned green when the person behind him honked his horn (the cell phone guy was too distracted to catch the light change). Well the cell phone man was short-tempered and began screaming into his rear view mirror at the honker behind him, and with a heavy foot on the gas, shot out into the intersection without looking. He was side-swiped by a speeder (by this time the light had changed back to red) and killed. Someone had made the comment that it was a tragic way to go, screaming at the rear view mirror.

"If he were a cow," said Justin, "he'd be the steak an otherwise placid man would eat and then go home and pick a fight with his wife for no apparent reason."

Then there was the comment he made about smell, how changes in the weather are not about looking skyward or checking thermometers, but rather about getting close to the earth and letting the nasal passages do their work. He can sniff out a storm days in advance. He can't say exactly how, only that it's a feeling he gets that's triggered by aromatic sensations, a feeling that's been far more consistent than the Channel 7 weather reports.

But the most peculiar thing Justin does—that he never did before the accident—is sit on the bluff above his beloved closeout. He likes to spend his afternoons there, feel the sun crawl slowly down his back. He'll sit there for hours, listening to the ocean, sniffing at fallen leaves, rocking slowly forward and back. What's strange are the fingers in his right hand; he keeps them moving about nervously, as though he were doing fingerboard stunts not on his little half pipe but to a tune in his head. It was only recently that we put together the finger twitches with the sound of the breaking waves, and realized Justin was actually reliving those "runs" he used to make in his high school years, some of the most original surfing any of us had ever seen.

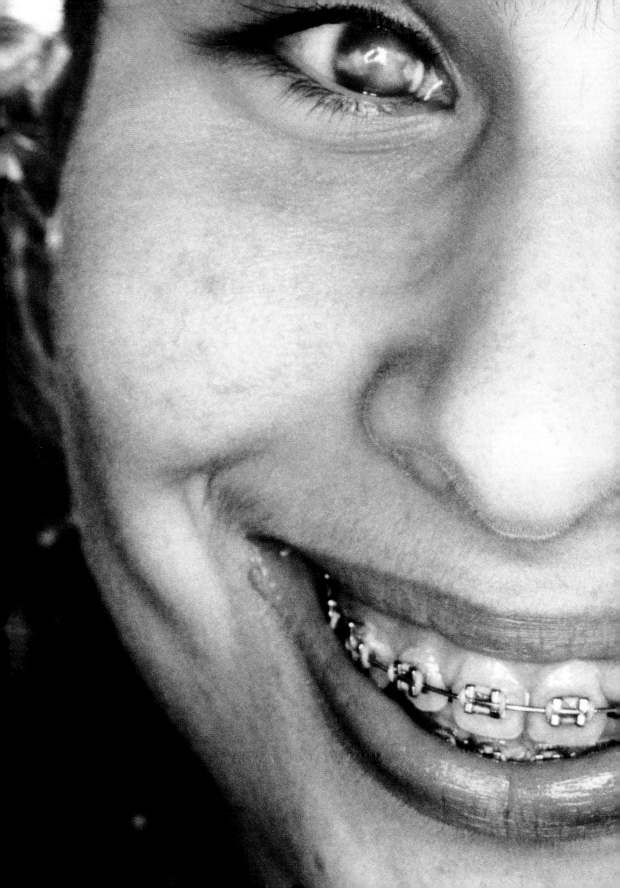

AMELIA, BLIND SURFER

NOW'S THE TIME

Scene: Four surfers huddled around the dining room table of a typical North Shore beachfront abode. The room is filled with surfboards, camera equipment and empty beer cans. Outside, a stormy west swell thunders across the reef. The windows shake.

"The all-time scene in Willy Wonka and the Chocolate Factory…" Derek Spine starts to stay and leaves it hanging with his trademark dramatic pause.

He's slumped back in his chair, his chestnut Monkees haircut a shoddy mess. He wears a turquoise bowling shirt and has the face of a bald eagle. Rings of smoke swirl up to the lampshade above him as he leans forward to tip a Cuervo bottle into a black coffee cup.

"…was the part where Wonka was making his grand appearance and he was a cripple, an old fragile man with a cane, and the camera flashed on all the kids and their looks of disappointment and as quickly as their universes had shattered, Wonka stopped, dropped his cane, began to tip over like an old guy and then turned it into that magnificent somersault."

Derek twirls his fingers in front of his face.

"I'll be Harry Houdini's rabbit out of a hat…" Art Skewer mutters out the corner of his mouth, a cheap cigar between his teeth.

Art's a hefty man—6'3" and somewhere around 300 lbs. His jet-black hairline recedes, his eyes are the color of hydroponically grown marijuana, and his facial expressions are punctuated by a jagged single eyebrow. His chubby hands shuffle the deck of cards with Vegas precision. He peels the top one off and slides it toward Derek.

"Wonka wasn't a candy man," Art says, tossing cards around the table. "He was a magician, an alchemist. He turned chocolate into a religious experience."

"I'll be a fortune teller's crystal ball…What about Roald Dahl, the guy that wrote the book?" Kelly Yater says with his mouthful. "They say he foresaw the whole thing in a dream. The story that would morph from a fictional book to a fictional movie to a non-fictional candy company…*that he'd sell!*—the 'Wonka' name, myth, everything—for an even more non-fictional twelve and a half million dollars."

Yater brings the yellow bag to his face and reads aloud: "Willy Wonka's Shock Tarts, Gummi Blast with Shock Crystals. Distributed by Nestle USA, Inc."

"I'll be a rusty nail bursting a pale pink bubble," Brock Middle says in a been there/done that tone. He points about the table with his cigar like it's a magic wand: "There's no greater sin than the desecration of a child's spirit…"

He puffs from the cigar, no hands. Teeth and gums compose his face, a long ash defies gravity, and as he speaks, smoke leaks from every orifice in his head. "…And we mustn't forget that on occasion Wonka did that." He reaches for the tequila bottle. "The more I think about it the more I say you can keep your Custers, JFKs, Clint Eastwoods, Willy Wonkas… There's never been a greater American hero than Thurston Howell III!"

"Shoots!" says Kelly Yater, cracking his knuckles.

In the middle of a circular koa wood table is a shiny stack of quarters. Around it are bottles, cups and candy. Art Skewer flicks out the last card and the players scoop them up, staring intently at their hands. After a beat or two the attention turns to Derek Spine.

"Hit the deck, hit the hay, hit the piñata at a Tijuana princess's four-year-old birthday party," Derek says in a fruity manner. "And Arty, you too can hit me."

Art flicks a card to Derek. It's the three of clubs.

"I'm good," Derek says.

Art nods to Kelly. "What'll it be, kid?"

"I'll be Jesus walking on water and turning it into wine," Kelly says, twirling two cards in one hand with just a little bit of abracadabra. He flicks a Shock Tart up in the air and catches it in his mouth. "The only difference between Wonka and a crazy man is that Wonka wasn't crazy."

Kelly contemplates his cards: "I'll go one more," he says.

Art flicks his wrist. The queen of hearts lands in Kelly's lap. He picks it up, slides it into his hand and thinks a moment. "I'm cool," he says.

Art turns to Brock.

"I'll be a primordial man's scraped knuckle…" Brock Middle says, "You can hit me."

Five of diamonds lands next to a bottle of Guinness Stout.

"I'll be a Wall Street stockbroker's high blood pressure," he says shuffling his three cards. "We go again."

Art flicks out the ten of clubs.

"I'll be the flashing red lights in a drunk driver's rear view mirror," Brock says, slapping the table. He tosses his cards on the table. "I'm out."

Now it's Arty's turn. He rubs his big hands together like a big bear about to eat a big fish. He gives a proprietary gaze to the shiny stack of quarters at the center of the table. With his eyes shut he scoops up his cards, turns them to face the others, and shows them around the table: *ace of clubs, queen of diamonds.*

"I'll be an Everlasting Gobstopper, he says with his eyes still closed: "Black Jack."

A Q 7 5 3
♣ ♦ ♠ ♣ ♦

LA FAMILIA
ETERNO

IN PANAMA THERE WAS
A SURF CONTEST THAT
WAS MORE LIKE A WOODSTOCK
& WAS LESS ABOUT THE
ACTION IN THE WATER
THAN IT WAS ABOUT
THE BEAUTY ON THE BEACH.

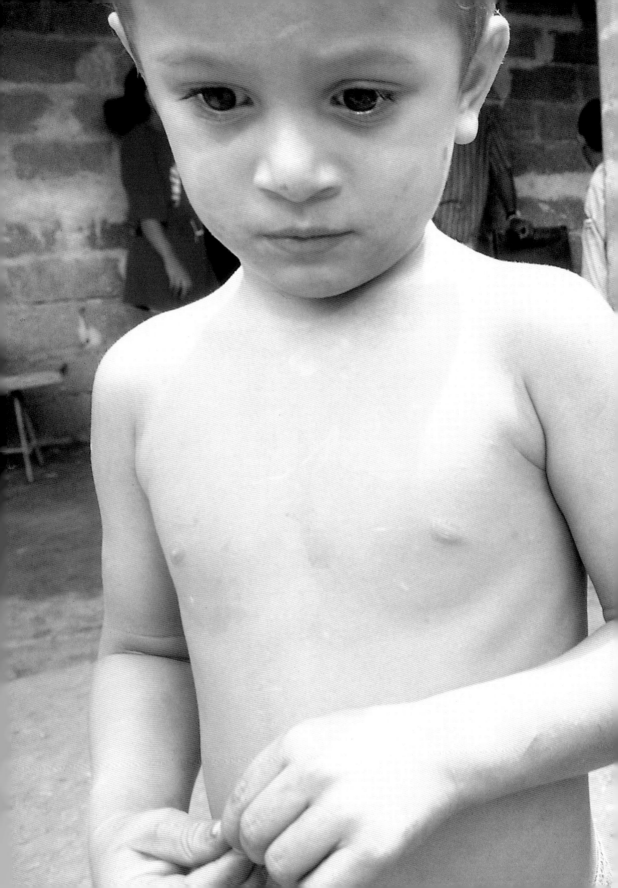

A COUPLE OF QUEENS

00340811   (949) 300-7233   10/02/
        093428   BRISICK, JAMES

        030 31 W STREET 33

Rent 03786 -001 NEW YORK STORIES   10/04/01   3.75
Payment - Ca   3.75

+ A LONG STRING OF KNIGHTS

FROM THE INSIDE LOOKING OUT OF A BAR ON AVE. A

Man walks up to the window. I'm inside a Japanese restaurant/bar/gallery/discotech and the man looks European. He makes faces at me then out comes a pet baby squirrel from his tattered backpack. He has a slightly crazed look on his face and pulls a long drag from his cigarette. His hands look like they could use a good wash. He's maybe somebody's father and definitely somebody's son. There's a chance he sleeps on the street. His focus hones right in on me; a minor league version of a seal trainer at Sea World picking a kid out of the audience to participate in his tricks, though the squirrel doesn't do tricks but runs about the grimy fella's shoulders frightfully, and I'm not a kid called "Billy" but a grown man a couple of Heinekens into a nervous night. The only thing that separates the geniuses from the junkies who play chess at the park are a coupla queens and a long string of knights. The only thing separating me from this squirrel man is a wall of glass and about two week's worth of showers. There are approximately 1,643 bars, 914 squirrels, and 6,032 homeless folk in the downtown section of Manhattan. This tale is about only three of them.

IF YOU CAN'T BEAT 'EM JOIN 'EM
(HERE A FUCK THERE A FUCK EVERYWHERE A FUCK FUCK)

There's never any hot water at 300 E. 15th Street. The reason for this is because there's always a lot of showering going on—there's always a lot of showering going on 'cause of the couple who live in Apt. A on the first floor. Never in my life have I known such virile, sadomasochistic, prolific sex hounds. How do I know this? 'Cause I sleep on a thin futon that sits atop the thin floor that separates me from where their sex wars happen on a 24/7 basis…It literally never stops, and so one night, after listening to them go at it for the sixth or seventh time in about as many hours, I decided to take a walk downstairs just to get a look at what the entrance to their fuckdungeon looks like. What I saw was Christian idolatry on the front door (crucifix, rosary beads, Mother Mary with halo) and what I heard was *"fuck you.. no fuck you… NO FUCK YOU!"* and then the slamming and slapping and panting that accompanies supercharged, somewhat twisted beautiful fucking.

This has become my soundtrack, my sexual alarm clock, my call to arms and legs and nipples and loins…They spur the desire in me, and then I pass it on to my immediate neighbors, and then it dominoes about the building; one apartment across to the next, a neverending echo chamber of passionate wails, guttural moans, synchronized gasps and ultraloud *FUCK YOU*s that can usually be traced back to Apt. A on the first floor. It's as though somewhere in the building, at all times, there's a fleet of galloping horses moving their way toward orgasm (eyes are sunken just a little bit further back into the skulls of those who inhabit this building and afterglow has become an around-the-clock complexion).

And so this is why there's no hot water at 300 E. 15th Street; there are 18 apartments that seem to be either sexing or showering all the fuck-long day. And this has come to penetrate my every thought, every thumbprint, all aspects of my life, including this book. Had I written this living next door to an ashram where chants and *Om*s floated about my subconscious, the content may have been entirely different. But I don't. I live above a couple of sick lovers.

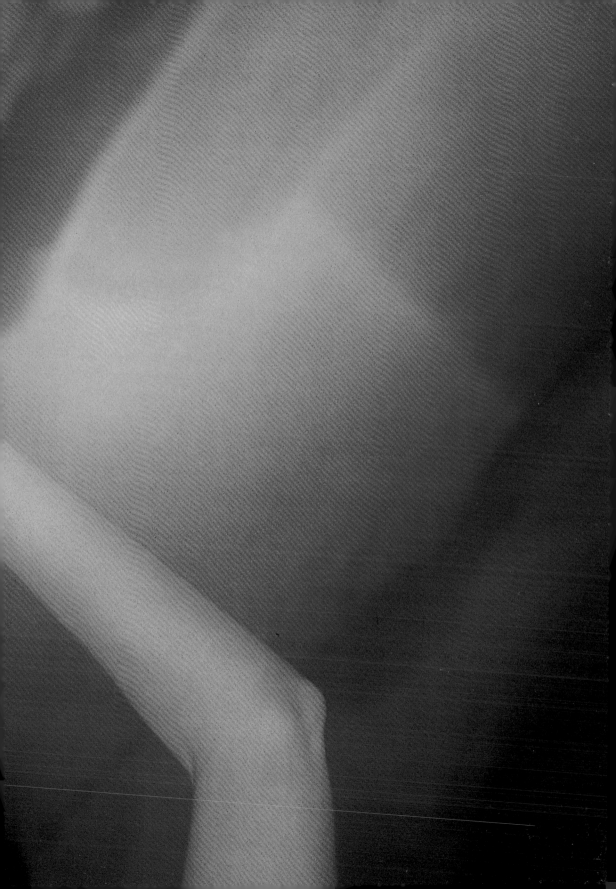

WORDS + PICTURES BY JAMIE BRISICK
DESIGNED BY STACI MACKENZIE
PUBLISHED BY CONSAFOS PRESS
PRINTED BY AMERICAN BOOK

DEDICATED TO KEVIN JAMES BRISICK
1964 · 1987

THANKS TO: KIRK GEE, CRAIG MARSHALL,
GREG DELLA STUA, VAVA RIBEIRO, STEPHEN
MALE, SIMONE LEWIS, MARCUS SANDERS,
DANIELA VILLAS BOAS, SANDOW BIRK,
O'RAVENSCROFT, SCOOTER LEONARD,
STEVE SIEGRIST, MARCELO JUNEMANN,
BRAILLE INSTITUTE, NICK CARROLL,
A+I COLOR, FRIENDS, FAMILY,
+ ALL THE PEOPLE + PLACES IN THE BOOK

PRINTED IN HONG KONG
DISTRIBUTED FROM LOS ANGELES BY:
CONSAFOS PRESS
P.O. BOX 931568
LOS ANGELES, CA 90093 USA